Penguin

GW01086594

GHOST
STORIES

M. R. JAMES

LEVEL

3

RETOLD BY KATE WILLIAMS
ILLUSTRATED BY TAYLOR DOLAN
SERIES EDITOR: SORREL PITTS

PENGUIN BOOKS

UK | USA | Canada | Ireland | Australia
India | New Zealand | South Africa

Penguin Books is part of the Penguin Random House group of companies
whose addresses can be found at global.penguinrandomhouse.com.
www.penguin.co.uk www.puffin.co.uk www.ladybird.co.uk

Penguin Readers edition of *Ghost Stories* published by Penguin Books Ltd, 2021
003

Original text written by M. R. James
Text for Penguin Readers edition adapted by Kate Williams
Text for Penguin Readers edition copyright © Penguin Books Ltd, 2021
Illustrated by Taylor Dolan
Cover illustration by Ed Kluz
Illustrations copyright © Penguin Books Ltd, 2021

Printed and bound in Great Britain by Clays Ltd, Elcograf S.p.A.

The authorized representative in the EEA is Penguin Random House Ireland, Morrison Chambers,
32 Nassau Street, Dublin D02 YH68

A CIP catalogue record for this book is available from the British Library

ISBN: 978-0-241-52070-3

All correspondence to:
Penguin Books
Penguin Random House Children's
One Embassy Gardens, 8 Viaduct Gardens,
London SW11 7BW

MIX
Paper | Supporting
responsible forestry
FSC
www.fsc.org   FSC® C018179

Penguin Random House is committed to a
sustainable future for our business, our readers
and our planet. This book is made from Forest
Stewardship Council® certified paper.

Contents

New words

blanket

curtains

ghost

golf

suitcase

whistle

concert

envelope

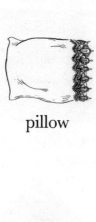

pillow

programme

bone

crown

sand

track

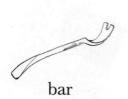

bar

devil

handle

Note about the stories

Montague Rhodes James (1862–1936) is famous for his ghost stories. He wrote the four stories in this book between 1904 and 1925.

James studied at the University of Cambridge, and later he was a **historian*** there. He liked to tell ghost stories to his friends in Cambridge at Christmas.

Many of his stories happen by the sea in Suffolk, in East Anglia, in the east of England. James knew Suffolk well because he lived there when he was a child.

Before-reading questions

1 Look at the cover of the book, then look quickly at the pictures in the book. Which sentences are true, do you think?
  a The stories happened a few years ago.
  b All the stories happen in London.
  c People in the stories feel frightened.
2 Look at the definition of "curse" and "cursed" on page 78. What might happen to someone if they are cursed?
3 What old things do people find in the ground? Have you ever found anything very old? What was it? What did you do with it?
4 Which numbers are lucky or unlucky in your country? What do people do differently because of these numbers?

*Definitions of words in **bold** can be found in the glossary on pages 78–80.

Whistle and I'll Come to You

Professor Parkins was having dinner at Cambridge University, the day before the spring holidays.

"What are your plans for the holidays, professor?" asked the man next to him.

"I'm going to Burnstow to play golf," replied Parkins. He was a **serious** young man, and he wanted to learn to play better.

"Do you mean Burnstow in Suffolk?" said the man. His name was Disney, and he was a professor of **archaeology**. "This morning I read about an **archaeological site** there. If you have time, could you tell me if it looks interesting? It's north of the town, close to the beach, half a mile from the Globe Hotel."

"I'm staying at the Globe, so I will look, of course," agreed Professor Parkins. "Many of the hotels in Burnstow are still closed after the winter and I don't know if I'm going to be comfortable at the Globe. I wanted a large room, and they have given me one with an **extra** bed. But I don't need two beds, so I'm not very happy about that."

Another man was listening, and he began to laugh. He thought that Professor Parkins was too serious. "I'd like a holiday by the sea," he said with a smile. "I can come after a few days and use the extra bed, if you like."

Parkins did not like this idea because he wanted to be on his own, but he did not want to be **rude**.

"That's a good idea, Mr Rogers, but I think that you may be bored. I'm going to play golf every day."

"I won't come if you don't want me to," said Rogers, laughing again. "But maybe I can help to keep the ghosts out of your room."

Parkins looked angry. He thought that Mr Rogers was rude. "You know that I don't **believe in** ghosts, and I don't like talking about them. It's not a serious **subject**. But come to Burnstow later in the week, if you like."

The next day, Parkins travelled to Burnstow and found the Globe Hotel. His room with two beds was large and the windows looked three ways. One window looked north, along the beach, one window looked south, towards the town, and the middle window looked straight at the grey sea.

Parkins took his clothes out of his suitcase and put them away tidily. Then he was ready to go out to play golf. He played all afternoon with another hotel **guest**, an older man with a red face, a big grey moustache and a very loud voice. By the end of the afternoon Parkins wanted to get away from **Colonel** Wilson. "I think that he has shouted at soldiers all his life," thought Parkins. "Now I really need a quiet walk before dinner."

So Parkins decided to walk down the beach and look for Professor Disney's archaeological site. The ground was not flat at the top of the beach and in one place he fell over a large stone under the grass. When he got up, he looked closely at the ground. He could see a lot more big stones below the grass, in a large circle.

"This might be Disney's site," he thought, feeling excited. He pulled away some grass and studied the stones. Then he moved some **earth** between two stones and found a **hole** in the ground below them. It was big enough to put his hand inside.

"What's this?" he thought, when his fingers touched something cold and hard. He was sure that it was not a stone, so he pulled it out. It was getting dark, but he could see that the thing was metal and very old. It was about the size of his little finger. He put it safely into his coat and began to walk back.

A cold wind was **blowing** off the sea and the sky was getting dark quickly. There was just a little light in the west, then the dark grey sky, the empty beach and the quiet noise of the sea. Once, Parkins looked back at the site and was happy to see that he was not the only man on the beach. There was someone behind him. The person was walking quickly but not getting any nearer. Parkins knew that it was stupid, but in this quiet and empty place he could not stop thinking of the frightening ghost stories from his old children's books.

"I must **hurry** or I'll be late for dinner," he thought, and he began to run.

He met Colonel Wilson for dinner, and then they played a quiet game of cards. When he went upstairs to bed, Parkins decided that he was happy with his holiday.

"I will enjoy my two weeks here," he thought.

Seeing his coat on the back of his door, Parkins suddenly remembered the little metal thing from the hole at Disney's site. He took it out, cleaned it and looked at it closely. He could see now that it was a whistle, but it was full of earth. Being a tidy man, he pushed the earth out on to a piece of paper with his knife and carried the paper to the window. When he opened the window, he was very surprised to see someone outside on the beach.

"People stay out very late here in Burnstow," Parkins thought. Then he held the whistle up to the light and cleaned it some more. Now he could see some words on it:

Quis Est Iste Qui Venit

"That is Latin," Parkins thought. "I think it means 'Who is coming?' or something like that. Well, maybe the answer is to whistle for him."

He put the whistle to his mouth and **blew** very softly. He was surprised at the noise. It was soft, but he felt that it travelled a long way. And then it made a picture in his head. He could see a long dark beach, with the wind blowing and a **figure** in the middle. He blew the whistle again, a little louder.

Suddenly, a strong wind came through the open window. Parkins ran to the window and tried to close it, pushing against the wind. But the wind was too strong and it felt like he was pushing against a strong man. Then, just as suddenly as before, the wind stopped and the window closed.

When Parkins went to bed, he felt too **nervous** to sleep. Then he heard a noise. But another guest was just moving in their bed and Parkins felt a little better knowing that another person also could not sleep. He lay with his eyes closed, thinking of the wind, and the whistle, and the picture of the figure on the beach in his head.

He could see the long, empty beach again, but the figure was closer. He could see that it was a man and that he was running away from something. The man looked very frightened and, every few seconds, he turned and looked behind him. It was becoming harder for him to run, and he kept falling down. Now Parkins could see something light, moving down the beach. Its strange white clothes were blowing in the wind. It stopped, put its arms above its head and ran quickly across the beach towards the sea. Then it ran back up the beach, getting nearer and nearer to the man.

When the frightening white figure was close behind the man, Parkins could not keep his eyes shut any longer. He sat up in bed, got out his book and read until he fell asleep.

After breakfast the next morning, a servant came to his room.

"I've brought an extra blanket because it is cold," she said to Parkins. "Which bed shall I put it on?"

"Please put it on that one, of course," Parkins said, pointing at his bed. "Didn't you see earlier that I slept in that bed? You made it tidy while I was at breakfast."

"I'm sorry, professor. I thought that you tried both beds last night. It looked like someone slept in the other bed, too, so I also made that one tidy."

"Well, I'm very sorry to give you more work. Maybe I put my suitcase on the bed yesterday, when I took out my clothes," Parkins explained. Then he remembered Mr Rogers. "A friend of mine is coming from Cambridge the day after tomorrow. Is it all right if he uses the extra bed?"

"Of course, professor," replied the servant, and she went out, leaving Parkins to get ready for golf. He met Colonel Wilson a short while later, outside the hotel.

"Did you hear the strange wind last night?" said Colonel Wilson. "Have you heard about people whistling for the wind when they want it to blow? It sounded to me like someone whistled for the wind last night because it came so suddenly."

"I must tell you, Colonel, that I don't believe in crazy things like that," replied Parkins. "If something is not possible, then I don't believe in it. I blew a whistle twice last night and then the wind came, but–"

The colonel looked at him. "You blew a whistle last night?"

"Yes. I found it yesterday," said Parkins.

Then Parkins told the colonel everything about the archaeological site and finding the whistle.

The colonel was very surprised.

"We don't know anything about that site. There might be **magic** in it. I don't think that you should blow that whistle," he said. "It might be dangerous."

"That's crazy! I told you that I don't believe in magic," replied Parkins.

They played golf together all day, and then walked back to the hotel. When they got near, a young boy ran around a corner of the building, straight into the colonel. The boy looked very frightened and began to cry.

"What's the matter?" Colonel Wilson asked him. "What has made you afraid?"

"Something was waving at me from the window," cried the boy. "I couldn't see it very well, but it was a horrible white figure."

"Which window was it? Show me," said Colonel Wilson.

The boy took them to the front of the hotel and pointed. Then he ran away fast.

"That's very strange," said Parkins. "That's *my* window. Colonel, will you come upstairs with me to look? I hope that the servants haven't been in my room while I was out."

When they got to his room, Parkins looked at the beds. "I thought that the servant made that bed tidy this morning. But look, the blankets and **sheets** are not tidy now," he said. "But it doesn't matter. I'll speak to her later."

Then Parkins went to get the whistle and he showed it to Colonel Wilson.

"What are you going to do with it?" asked Colonel Wilson.

"When I get back to Cambridge, I'll show it to a professor of archaeology there," Parkins replied.

"I think that you should throw it into the sea," said the colonel. "It might have some strange **power**.

But I know that we'll never agree about that."

That night, the moon was bright and when Parkins went to bed, he saw that there were no curtains at the window. "It didn't matter last night, because there was no moon," he thought. "But I don't want the moonlight to wake me up tonight." So he used a walking stick and an umbrella to hold up a blanket in front of the window. Then he got into bed, read a few pages and soon went to sleep.

About an hour later, a terrible noise woke him up. He opened his eyes and saw the walking stick, the umbrella and the blanket all on the floor. He saw the moon through the window. He lay for a few minutes, thinking. "Should I get up and put the blanket back over the window?" he thought. "If I don't, will I be able to sleep?"

Then he listened hard. Something in the other bed was moving and making a noise. Was it a cat? No, it was making too much noise for a cat.

Suddenly, he saw a figure sit up in the bed. Parkins jumped out of bed and ran across the room to get his walking stick from the floor. But this was a terrible mistake. While he was at the window, the figure got up from the bed. It stood between the two beds, in front of the door, with its arms above its head. Parkins watched, feeling very afraid. He could not go past it to get to the door. "Has this ghost come because I blew the whistle?" Parkins thought.

The figure began to move towards Parkins's bed, waving its arms in front of it. Parkins suddenly understood that it could not see. He watched it feel all around the bed and find that it was empty. Then it moved into the light of the moon and he could see its horrible face. Parkins was **terrified**. One corner of its strange white clothes touched his own face, and he gave a loud cry.

Hearing the cry, the figure jumped at Parkins and pushed him against the window. The window opened, the horrible face came closer and closer, and the terrified Parkins moved back. He was falling out of the window. At the last second, the door opened and Colonel Wilson ran in.

But when he hurried to the two figures at the window, only Parkins was there. He was lying on the floor and next to him there were just blankets and sheets.

Colonel Wilson asked no questions. He put Parkins back into bed and slept in the other bed.

In the morning, Colonel Wilson came out of the room, carrying the whistle. He took it down to the sea and threw it a very long way into the water. Then he went back to the hotel and saw that a servant was carrying some blankets and sheets to a fire in the garden.

The next day, Mr Rogers arrived early from Cambridge and Parkins was very happy to see him. From that day, he never wanted to go on holiday on his own again. His ideas about ghosts changed, too. Seeing white sheets blowing on a washing line sometimes made him nervous, and a blanket on the back of a chair at night often stopped him sleeping.

Karswell's Curse

Mrs Gayton and her husband were walking to her cousin's house near the British Museum in London. Mr Gayton looked worried.

"What's the matter?" Mrs Gayton asked him. "Is something wrong at work?" Mr Gayton **published** books and **papers** about **history**.

"I had another angry letter this morning," he replied. "The same man keeps writing to me."

"Who is he?" asked Mrs Gayton.

"He's a very rich man from Warwickshire called Mr Karswell," answered her husband.

"My cousin and his wife have a second house in Warwickshire. Maybe they know him," she said.

"I don't think that they will know Karswell. He's not a nice man," he said.

"What have you done to make him angry?" she asked.

"He has written a paper about the history of **black magic**, and he sent it to me to publish. I sent it to Edward Dunning to **review** because he's the best person in England on this subject. He thought that it was very bad and that I should not publish it. I wrote to Mr Karswell to tell him, but of course I didn't give him Dunning's name. Mr Karswell is very angry about it. He keeps writing to ask me about the **review** and the name of the person, but I'll never tell him."

"Yes, it may be very bad for Edward if Mr Karswell learns his name," agreed Mrs Gayton.

Edward Dunning was a good friend of the Gaytons and Mrs Gayton was worried for him. She decided to speak to her cousin about Karswell at lunch.

"Yes, I have heard of him," her cousin told her. "And I even saw him this morning. He was coming out of the British Museum."

"Do you know him? What is he like?" asked Mrs Gayton.

"He's a horrible man! He is rude, angry and never kind. About ten years ago, he wrote a book called *The **Mystery** of Magic*. My friend, John Harrington, gave it a bad review," he said.

"Didn't John Harrington have a horrible accident?" said Mrs Gayton.

"Yes. He fell out of a tree and broke his neck. It was terrible. He was walking down a country road on his own late at night. He suddenly became very frightened and climbed up the tree. So what happened to him? Why did he do that? His brother, Henry, has never been able to understand it."

At home, Mrs Gayton said to her husband, "I hope that you can keep Edward Dunning's name a secret from that horrible man, Karswell."

"I won't tell Karswell, of course," said Mr Gayton. "But he might ask questions at the British Museum library. And if I tell the **librarians** not to speak about Dunning, I will have to explain more. Let's just hope that Karswell won't ask them."

But Karswell was a clever man.

A few days later, Edward Dunning was travelling home on the bus from the British Museum library. He was a **historian**, and he studied in the library nearly every day.

It was too dark to read his book, so he looked at the **advertisements** on the windows opposite him. Suddenly, he saw a new one with blue letters.

JOHN HARRINGTON,
DIED ON THE 18TH OF SEPTEMBER, 1909.
HE HAD THREE MONTHS.

Dunning thought that this was very strange, so he wrote down the words. When he got off the bus, he asked the driver about it, but the driver knew nothing. The next morning, Dunning got on the same bus and looked for the advertisement, but it was not there.

That evening, another strange thing happened. Dunning was walking down a quiet street near his house. A man on the corner was holding some paper advertisements, but nobody took one. When Dunning passed him, the man put an advertisement into his hand and Dunning felt a little **shock**. He looked down at the paper in his hand and saw the name Harrington again in large blue letters. The next minute, another man hurried past him and took the paper out of his hand. Dunning quickly looked all around him, but the man was gone.

The next day, Dunning was back at his desk in the British Library, but he was feeling worried and found it difficult to work. He could not stop thinking about the name "John Harrington" in blue letters. "Two strange things have happened to me this week," he thought. "What does it mean?"

Suddenly, he thought that someone behind him was saying his name. He turned around quickly and some of his books and papers fell on the floor. But there was nobody there. Dunning put his things back on his desk and then saw a man near him. He was holding out a book.

"May I give you this?" said the man. "I think that it is yours."

"Yes, it is mine," replied Dunning. "Thank you." But the man was already walking away.

Dunning went to speak to the librarian. "Who is that man?" he asked her.

"He's a man called Karswell," the librarian replied. "A few days ago, he asked me for the name of the most important historian in England on the subject of magic. Of course, I gave him your name. Shall I run after him?"

"No!" cried Dunning. "Please don't! I want to keep away from him."

"All right," said the librarian. "He doesn't come here very often, so I don't think that you'll meet him."

Dunning usually enjoyed his evenings at home on his own, but this evening he felt nervous about going back to his quiet house. When he got to his door, he was very surprised to see the doctor coming out.

"I'm very sorry to say that both your servants are **seriously** ill," the doctor told him. "I have sent them to hospital. I think that they have eaten something dangerous."

"How could that happen?" asked Dunning, feeling more worried than ever.

"A man came to the house at lunchtime selling fish and they bought some. Maybe the fish made them ill," replied the doctor. "But the strange thing is that this man did not sell fish to any other houses in the street today. Your servants will be in hospital for a few days, so why don't you come and have dinner with me tonight?"

Dunning was very happy to agree, and he did not go back to his empty house until 11:30 p.m. He went straight to bed and lay in the dark, trying to sleep. Suddenly, he heard a door open downstairs, and he jumped out of bed. He hurried out to the **corridor** and listened at the top of the stairs. But everything was quiet, and he could see no lights downstairs. He went back into his bedroom, turned the key in the door and got back into bed.

He lay down, put his hand under the pillow and got the most horrible shock. His fingers touched a mouth, with teeth, and hair around it. He was sure that it was not the mouth of a person.

Dunning was terrified. In just a few seconds, he was out of bed, out of his room and safely inside another room. There he passed a terrible night, listening for noises and feeling very frightened. Early the next morning, he went **nervously** back to his bedroom. He looked under the pillow, but there was nothing there. Everything looked normal, but he still felt very afraid.

"What am I going to do today?" he thought. "I don't want to go to the British Museum library because Karswell might be there. But I don't want to stay in this empty house."

So, first, he went to the hospital to visit his servants, and then he went to eat lunch in a restaurant. He was happy to see two friends there, but Mr and Mrs Gayton got a shock to see Dunning's white and worried face.

He told them about the horrible things that happened at his house the day before.

"You mustn't go home to an empty house," said Mrs Gayton. "Come and stay with us."

That evening, Dunning told them about Karswell. "He was at the British Museum library yesterday. I think that he knows that I read his book."

"I don't think that the man is dangerous. Everything will be all right, if you keep away from him," said Mr Gayton.

But Mrs Gayton saw that Dunning still looked very frightened. "What's the matter?" she asked. "What are you worried about?"

"Do you know anything about a man called John Harrington?" Dunning replied.

Mrs Gayton was **shocked**. "Yes. Why?"

Then, Dunning told them about the advertisement on the bus and the paper in the street, both with John Harrington's name on.

"I only know that he died suddenly ten years ago," Mrs Gayton said. She did not want to tell Dunning about John Harrington's terrible accident and make him even more worried. "But John had a brother called Henry," she said. "He might know more. If you'd like to meet him, I'll ask my cousin for Henry Harrington's address."

Dunning agreed and a few days later he and Henry Harrington met. Dunning told him about the two advertisements with John's name on, and about his servants and his frightening night at home. Then Henry Harrington told Dunning about the mystery of his brother's accident.

"My brother was acting very strangely for a few weeks before he died," Harrington said. "He thought that someone was following him, and he talked to me about black magic. I don't know if I believe in that, but I also felt that someone wanted to hurt him. Maybe someone is trying to hurt you, too. Can you think of anyone?"

"Yes, I think that I can," said Dunning. "I gave a writer a bad review, and I **believe** that he is angry with me."

"My brother did the same thing! Is that person called Karswell?" asked Harrington.

"Yes, he is!" Dunning was very shocked to hear that it was the same man.

"Then I must tell you more about my brother," said Harrington. "John loved music and often went to listen to it. Once, he was at a concert and he lost his programme. So the man next to him gave him his programme to keep. That night, my brother felt very nervous but he did not understand it. I visited him the next day and we sat together by the fire, talking about the concert. When he opened the programme to show me, he found a small piece of paper inside. The paper had some very strange writing on it and John thought that it might be important. So he decided to look for the man at the next concert and give the programme back to him. But suddenly the piece of paper blew into the fire.

"'You can't give it back to the man now,' I told John, and he was angry with me.

"'Why do you keep saying that?' he asked me. But I didn't understand him because I only said it once. I was worried that my brother was going crazy.

"After John died, I read Karswell's book about black magic, and I was very shocked. The writing was very bad, but the subject was also frightening. One chapter was about putting a **curse** on someone and Karswell knows his subject very well. I think that the writing on the paper was a curse. Karswell wanted my brother to die. Maybe John died because he couldn't give the paper back to Karswell. But if you can give the paper back, maybe you can break the curse."

Then Dunning told Harrington about his last visit to the British Museum library. "Karswell was there. Some of my books fell on the floor and he gave one back to me," he said. "We must go to your house and check that book now," said Henry. "There may be something inside it."

They hurried together to Dunning's house, and he got out the book. When Dunning opened it, a very thin, light piece of paper fell out and blew towards the open window. Harrington ran to the window and quickly closed it.

The two men looked at the paper and saw that it

had strange writing on it, too.

"This is just like my brother's paper. You must give it back to Karswell and only you can do it. But Karswell must not know that it's you, so you'll need to look different. You must cut off your beard and wear different clothes."

Dunning looked very frightened. "But how long have I got before . . .?"

"My brother got the paper on the 18th of June, and he died three months later," Harrington said.

Dunning remembered the advertisement on the bus. It said "He had three months."

He looked at Harrington. "I saw Karswell at the library a week ago, on the 23rd of April," he said. "Does that mean that . . . that I'm going to die on the 23rd of July?"

"I'll help you to give the paper back," Harrington told him. "I'll watch Karswell and tell you when you can do it safely."

For the next few weeks, Dunning waited nervously for news about Karswell. Then, just a week before 23rd July, Dunning got a message from Harrington. It said, "Karswell is going to France. He is getting the train from London to Dover on Thursday the 21st of July at 9 p.m. I will follow him on to the train. You must get on the train at the last stop. Look for me on the train but don't speak to me. And remember the paper."

Thursday came and Dunning was ready. His beard was gone and he wore a new hat and coat. He waited nervously for the train at Croydon, the last stop before Dover. "If I can't give the paper back to Karswell, I will die," he kept thinking.

The train came into the station and Dunning could see Harrington at the window. He got on to the train and sat down near Karswell, without looking at Harrington. On the seat next to him, opposite Karswell, was Karswell's coat. But Dunning could not put the paper into the coat. To break the curse, he had to give it to Karswell, and Karswell had to take it from him.

Karswell looked nervous and got up from his seat to stand at a window. While he was there, Dunning looked at the man's bag. Maybe he could take it without Karswell seeing, put the paper into the bag and give the bag back to him. Or was that too dangerous? Karswell might be watching.

Karswell came back to his seat, but he did not sit down for long. He stood up again and when he did that, something fell quietly off his seat. It was the envelope with his tickets in. Dunning waited until Karswell turned away, then quickly took the envelope from the floor and put the paper inside. The next minute Karswell was back again.

"May I give you this? I think that it is yours,"

Dunning said to him, holding out the envelope.

Karswell looked at the envelope. "Yes, it is. Thank you," he said, and he quickly put it in his jacket.

For the last few minutes of the journey, Dunning felt terrified. Karswell might look in the envelope and see the paper.

When the train stopped at Dover, Karswell took his coat off the seat and stood up. Dunning and Harrington followed him off the train without speaking. Then Karswell walked towards the boat to France and Harrington walked behind him. He watched Karswell show his ticket to the man and walk on to the boat.

But the ticket man shouted after Karswell, "Your friend didn't show me his ticket!"

"What do you mean?" replied Karswell angrily, looking round.

"I'm sorry," said the man. "I thought there was someone with you, but it was just your coat."

Then Karswell was gone.

When Harrington told him about this, Dunning was still worried. "Is something frightening following Karswell now because of the curse? And did it follow your brother years ago? Did I do the right thing? Is Karswell going to die?" he asked. "Maybe we should send him a message."

"I don't think that we should," replied Harrington. "He is a murderer. But if you want to send him a message, then I won't stop you."

"I saw on his suitcase that he's travelling to Abbeville in France. I'll send a message to all the hotels in Abbeville. My message will say, 'Look in your envelope.' Then I will feel happier," said Dunning.

Dunning sent the message. But did Karswell get it and did he understand it? Nobody will ever know. We only know that on the afternoon of 23rd July, an Englishman called Karswell was outside a **church** when a stone fell from the top and killed him.

The Buried Crown

In April 1919, my friend, Henry Long, was on holiday in East Anglia. He was staying at the Bear Hotel in Seaburgh, Suffolk. There were not many other guests and the hotel was quiet. One evening after dinner, Long was reading in an upstairs sitting room of the hotel. Suddenly, the door opened and a young man looked in. His face was very white.

"May I come in?" he asked, nervously.

"Of course," Long said. "Anyone can use this sitting room."

The young man came in and shut the door behind him quickly. He sat down and opened a book, but Long saw that he did not want to read it.

"Is everything all right?" Long asked him.

"You'll think that I'm very strange, but I've had a shock. My name is Paxton. I'm on my own here and I'm very worried about something. Can you help me?"

"Of course," Long said. "What's the matter, Mr Paxton?"

The young man told Long his story.

"It began a week ago, when I visited a village called Froston to look at a church. An old man was there, working in the garden. While I was outside, looking at the stone above the door, he came to speak to me.

"'Are you interested in our old stories?' the old man asked me. 'Do you see the three crowns of East Anglia there?'

"'Yes, I do,' I answered.

"'A thousand years ago, the **Anglo-Saxons buried** a crown in the ground at a site near Seaburgh,' the old man told me. 'People believed then that the crown could stop foreign countries attacking East Anglia from the sea.'

"'Where is it? Do people know?' I asked him. I thought that the idea of looking for the buried crown was exciting.

"'Yes, they do, but they keep it secret. But I can tell you about the Ager family. They lived around Seaburgh for hundreds of years. They believed that they were the **guardians** of the crown. I knew old Nathaniel Ager. In the war of 1870 between France and Germany, he stayed at the site all the time. His son did the same thing in the next war, the Boer War in South Africa. His grandson, William, was the last guardian of the crown. He lived near the site, in a little house in North Field, and he watched the place every night from the beginning of the last war, in 1914. But he was not well, and he died when he was only twenty-eight.

"'Maybe staying outside at night in the winter made him worse. Before he died, he was very worried that there was no one to keep the crown safe after him. So now the crown has no guardian,' the old man finished.

"I found this story interesting," Paxton told Long. "I couldn't stop thinking about the crown, and I wanted to find the site. But that was a terrible mistake.

"The next day, I walked up to North Field. I found the house and spoke to the woman about William Ager. 'He was a friend of mine,' I told her. She thought that his story was very sad and that William became more seriously ill and died because he slept outside in winter.

"'Did he go down to the sea at night?' I asked her.

"'No, he went up that hill with trees on,' she said, pointing.

"I decided that I had to look for the crown," Paxton told Long. "I had to look for it at night. I'm not going to tell you everything – the important thing is that I found the crown."

"You found it?" Long said to the young man. He was very surprised. "That's **amazing**! No one has ever seen an Anglo-Saxon crown."

"I have," Paxton said, seriously. "But I need to put it back, and I don't know how."

"Why do you want to put it back?" Long cried. "You have found something amazing. You must give it to an **archaeologist**."

Paxton was not listening. He put his face in his hands and said again, "I need to put it back."

"Are you sure that you really have the crown?" Long asked. He was beginning to think that Paxton might be crazy.

"Yes, it's in my room. I'm not going to bring it in here, but you can come and look at it," replied Paxton.

Long got up and followed Paxton to his room.

The young man was even more nervous than before. He looked both ways along the corridor outside his room, hurried inside and shut the door quietly. Then he opened his suitcase and took out a small blanket with something under it. He laid it on the bed and opened the blanket.

Long could not believe his eyes. He was looking at an Anglo-Saxon crown. It was about a thousand years old. He put out his hand to touch it.

"No! Don't touch it!" said Paxton. "I'll do it."

Paxton held the crown up and turned it around. Long looked at it, **amazed**. Then Paxton laid it down, put the blanket around it again and put it back into his suitcase. His face looked white, and he did not say a word.

"Come back to the sitting room and we'll talk there," said Long.

"Please will you check that no one is in the corridor?" said Paxton. Long could not understand this, but he opened the door and looked out. There was no one there.

The two men went back to the sitting room. Paxton still looked very frightened.

"What shall I do?" he said.

"We must tell an archaeologist about it," said Long.

"No, no!" said Paxton. " I have to put it back, but I'm too afraid. There's always someone following me."

"I don't understand," said Long. "Who is following you?"

"It began when I first started looking for the

crown," Paxton said in a very quiet voice. "Every time I went to the site, at night, there was always someone watching me. But I could only see him from the corner of my eye. When I looked straight at him, he wasn't there. Now I am sure that he is angry with me. He did not want me to take the crown.

"When I first saw the crown in the ground, this feeling got worse. I felt that someone was very close behind me, nearly touching my back. Then when I pulled the crown out, I heard a horrible cry behind me. As soon as I heard the old man's story at the church in Froston, I really wanted to find the crown. But, when I found it, I did not feel happy – I felt terrible. Why didn't I just put it back?

"I walked back to the hotel in the dark, and I knew that the figure was always with me. But one minute I could see him, and the next minute I couldn't. I think that he has some power over my eyes. It was early morning when I got back to the town. Everyone looked at me strangely, but they looked a little behind me, not straight at me. Is it possible that they saw the figure behind me?

"So now what am I going to do? I might be able to put the crown back, but I am still **cursed**," Paxton cried. "I have made someone angry by touching it!"

Long wanted to help the young man. Was it true that the crown had some strange power?

"If you're sure that you must put it back, I'll help you," he said to Paxton.

"Oh, thank you," cried Paxton. "When can we do it? Can we go tonight?"

"We'll go now," said Long. "It's late, but not too late for a walk, and the moon is bright tonight."

Downstairs, the **landlord** opened the door for them and watched them go. Paxton was carrying the crown in the blanket, under his coat.

The streets of Seaburgh were quiet and empty. Long and Paxton walked up the dark road, past the church. They both felt that someone was watching them, but they never saw anyone.

When they got to the trees on the hill, Paxton was terrified. While the young man found the right place in the ground, Long held his coat, with the crown inside it. In the moonlight, he could see a line of dark trees, the church, some houses and the sea. But he felt that something wild and terrible was there with them, waiting to attack them.

"Give me the crown now," said Paxton. "But don't touch it. You must not help me because you might also be cursed."

Long held out the coat and Paxton took out the crown. He put it into the ground and buried it, then they walked quickly away.

The two men hurried back to the hotel.

The landlord was waiting in the hall, and he opened the door for them. He looked up and down the beach.

"I thought that someone was following you earlier," the landlord said. "But there were two of you, so I wasn't too worried."

"We didn't see anyone on our walk," Long told him. "Good night." Then he and Paxton hurried upstairs to the sitting room.

"You've done it," Long said, when the door was shut. "You've put the crown back safely. Maybe it was a mistake to touch it, but nothing bad has happened. And I won't tell anyone about it. Everything is going to be all right. I hope that you feel better now. When we walked there, I felt very nervous, too. I had the feeling that someone was following us. But it was all right when we came back."

But Paxton looked no better. "You don't need to be worried because you haven't touched it," he said. "But I am still cursed. I was wrong to take the crown. I don't feel that he's waiting outside for me now, but–" He stopped. "But thank you," he said. "You've been very kind."

"You should go to bed now and rest tomorrow morning," said Long. "I'll be out in the morning, but we can meet here in the afternoon and go for a walk."

Long slept well and felt much better the next morning. It was a beautiful spring day. He saw Paxton at breakfast, and he also looked better.

"I'll stay in the hotel this morning and come out for a walk with you this afternoon," he told Long.

In the afternoon, Long went straight to the sitting room. Paxton was there, reading a book.

"Are you ready for our walk?" Long asked. "I'll change my clothes and meet you in half an hour."

Paxton agreed, and thirty minutes later, Long went back to the sitting room. But Paxton was not there. He was not anywhere in the hotel.

"Have you seen Mr Paxton?" Long asked a servant.

"He has gone out," the servant replied. "He heard you calling his name outside, and he went to find you. I looked out of the window, but I couldn't see you. Mr Paxton ran that way down to the beach."

Long ran to the beach. He could see Paxton running and waving his walking stick. It looked like he was following someone. But a **mist** was coming off the sea and Long could not see very well. "Does he think that the person is me?" Long thought.

Then he looked down and saw two tracks in the sand. One of the tracks was a person's with shoes, the other was of someone without shoes. The first track was Paxton's, but Long was shocked when he studied the second track. They were not normal feet but just the bones of feet.

Long was very frightened to think that Paxton was running after this figure. It might suddenly stop, turn around and attack him.

"What will its horrible face look like?" Long thought. "And how could Paxton think that the figure is me?" Then he remembered Paxton saying, *"I think that he has some power over my eyes."*

The mist was thicker and now Long could not see Paxton any more. Then, ahead, Long could see a large round building on the beach. When he got there, he quickly climbed to the top and looked all around. But he could see nothing through the mist. He turned to climb down and suddenly heard a horrible laugh. The noise came from below and blew away into the mist. Long looked over the side of the building.

Paxton was lying dead at the bottom.

Long hurried down to him as fast as he could, but he could do nothing. The young man's mouth was full of sand and stones. Long looked at the tracks in the sand. They showed that Paxton ran around the building and straight into someone.

An old man was walking slowly down the beach towards him. "I saw the young man fall," he told Long.

"Was there anyone with him? Did someone attack him?" Long asked. The old man was not sure. He did not think that there was anyone there.

Long sent him to get help while he stayed behind.

"What will I tell the police when they come?" Long thought. "I can tell them that I met Paxton yesterday and that he was very nervous and worried. I can tell them about the tracks in the sand. But I can't tell them that the ghost of William Ager killed him because he touched the buried crown. I must not give away its secret."

Long never went to Seaburgh again.

Number 13

A few months ago, my cousin visited Viborg, a pretty old town next to the water in Denmark. He has never been back, and he will never go back, and I am going to tell you why.

In 1726 there was a terrible fire. But I am not writing about the history of Viborg – I only want to tell you about the Golden Lion Hotel.

My cousin, Mr Anderson, chose this hotel because it was a beautiful old building from before the fire. Mr Anderson is a professor of history, and he is very interested in old things. He was in Viborg because he wanted to study some old church books and papers.

He went into the Golden Lion Hotel and spoke to the landlord.

"I would like a large room because I need to study in there, too," he told the landlord.

"Number 17 is big and it's quiet," said the landlord, showing him the room.

"But it's too dark at the back of the hotel," said Anderson.

The landlord showed him two more rooms at the front of the hotel – Number 12 and Number 14. Both rooms were big and bright and had three windows on to the street. Anderson chose Number 12.

In hotels in Denmark it is normal to find the names of all the guests on the wall in the hall. While he waited for dinner, Anderson looked at these names, next to their room numbers. He saw that the Golden Lion did not have a room Number 13.

"That's interesting," Anderson thought. "Is that normal in Denmark, too, because the number thirteen is **unlucky**? I might ask the landlord about it tomorrow."

That night, Anderson got into bed at eleven o'clock. Then he remembered that his book was in his coat, outside the dining room, so he went quietly downstairs to get it. But, when he was back in the dark corridor outside his room, he could not open the door. He heard someone inside.

"Of course," Anderson thought. "This is the wrong door. But which room is this?" He looked at the number and saw that it was Number 13.

"But there isn't a Number 13 in this hotel," he thought, when he was back in his room. "And it's strange – my room looks smaller than before. But maybe I just think that it's smaller because I'm very tired."

The next morning, Anderson went to the library. He studied old books and papers all day, and he read about Viborg two hundred years before the fire. At that time, in the 1500s, the church owned many of the houses. A man called Nicolas Francken lived in one of these houses. He was not a good man. Some people even wrote that he sold his **soul** to the devil. Francken wanted to use black magic, and he paid for this power with his soul.

Anderson was interested in this house, but he could not find the address.

That evening, Anderson ate dinner at his hotel again and went upstairs to his room. In the corridor, he remembered something. "I forgot to ask the landlord about Number 13," he thought. "But is that room really there, or did I make a mistake last night?"

He looked for the door and there it was – Number 13. He listened for a minute outside the door and jumped when he heard a noise inside.

Anderson hurried into his room and was surprised again. His room looked smaller tonight, too. "But it doesn't matter," he thought. "I will ask the landlord for a different room tomorrow."

Then he looked for his suitcase, but he could not find it. It was not by the wall at the end of the room. "Maybe one of the servants has moved it. I will speak to the landlord in the morning," Anderson thought, and he took out a cigarette. He walked to the window on the right and looked out at the dark street. There was a tall building opposite with a wall and no windows. Anderson could see his own shadow on this wall, and on the left of his shadow he could see the shadow of the man in the next room, Number 11. On the right, he saw the shadow of the person in Number 13. The man looked tall and thin, and he was wearing something on his head.

"The man has a red light in his room because there's red light on the wall behind his shadow," Anderson thought.

Suddenly, there was a noise in the street and the man in Number 13 quickly stepped away from his window. Anderson put his cigarette down by the window and went to bed.

The next morning, when Anderson sat up in bed, he saw his suitcase at the end of the room. And he was happy to see that his room looked bigger again, in the light. But, when he went to the middle window, he was surprised to see his cigarette there. "That's very strange. I know that I was standing by the window on the right last night," he thought.

Then he left his room to go downstairs for breakfast and saw a man's shoes outside Number 13. He looked at the door, but now the number was 14.

"I don't usually make mistakes," Anderson thought, "but I've made three mistakes in twelve hours."

Anderson decided to think no more about it. He went back to the library, and he studied hard all day. He read some more about Nicolas Francken and learned that the man suddenly went away. But then he could find nothing more about him. "What happened to this strange man? Did he die suddenly?" Anderson thought.

That evening at dinner, Anderson saw the landlord and remembered to ask his question. "Why do most hotels in Denmark not have a room Number 13?" he asked.

The landlord laughed. "People don't want to stay in room Number 13 because the number 13 is unlucky. They say that it's better to sleep in the street than to stay in a room with that number!"

"Then what do you use your Number 13 for?" Anderson asked.

"There isn't a room Number 13," said the landlord.

Anderson began to feel worried. "Would you like to have a drink in my room when you've finished work?" he asked. He wanted to show the landlord Number 13.

The landlord happily agreed to visit him at ten o'clock and Anderson went upstairs to his room, without looking at Number 13. He wrote some letters, and just before ten o'clock he walked to the window. He could see the shadow of the man from Number 14 on the opposite wall but it was moving in a strange way, like he was dancing.

"The man from Number 14 is acting very strangely," Anderson thought. "Why is he dancing?"

Then Anderson heard the landlord at his door. The landlord looked surprised when he saw the room, but he said nothing. Anderson gave him a drink and they began to talk. But after a few minutes, they heard a terrible noise. Someone was singing – but it did not sound like normal singing.

The landlord's mouth was open, he looked afraid. "What's the matter with Mr Jensen in Number 14?" he said. "Why is he making that noise?"

Anderson did not have time to answer because Mr Jensen came into the room, looking very angry.

"Please stop that noise!" he said. But the horrible singing got louder, and he could see that it did not come from Anderson or the landlord.

"Where is it? Who is it?" cried Jensen. His face was white.

The landlord was holding the arms of his chair. He could not speak. Then the singing stopped and the singer laughed. After that, it was quiet.

"What is happening, landlord? Who is making that noise?" said Jensen.

"I don't know, but I never want to hear a noise like that again," answered the landlord.

"We must do something," said Anderson. "Let's all go and look at the next room."

"But that's Mr Jensen's room, and he is here," said the landlord.

"Mr Anderson is right. We must go and see," said Jensen.

They took a walking stick and an umbrella, and they left the room. It was very quiet in the corridor outside, but there was a light under the door of the next room. Jensen tried to turn the handle.

"I can't turn it," he said. "Landlord, go and get your strongest servant and bring something to open the door." The landlord was very happy to go downstairs while the other two men waited outside the door.

"It *is* Number 13, you see," said Anderson, looking at the door.

"Yes, there is your door, and there is mine," said Jensen.

"My room has three windows in the day," said Anderson. "But there are only two windows at night because my room gets smaller."

"My room is the same!" said Jensen. He had his back to the door when suddenly, it opened. A horrible arm with long grey hair on it came out and its fingers moved towards Jensen's neck.

Anderson shouted and quickly pulled Jensen away. The door closed and they heard a quiet laugh.

Jensen did not see anything, but he was very frightened. "Let's go together to one of our rooms," he said. "I don't want to be on my own."

But just then the landlord came back. The strong man with him was carrying a heavy metal bar.

When Anderson told them about the horrible arm, both the landlord and his servant went white.

"What am I going to do?" cried the landlord. "I have to do something or no guests will ever want to come to my hotel!"

"Is it normal for Danish men to be this frightened?" said Anderson, quickly. "Remember, there are four of us and one of him."

Anderson's words helped. Without waiting any longer, the servant hit the door hard with his metal bar.

But nothing happened. The door did not break and the heavy metal bar made only a soft noise. When the other three men looked, they saw only a wall. The door was gone. Room Number 13 was gone.

The four men looked at the wall. Then the landlord said, "Mr Anderson and Mr Jensen, maybe you would like a room with two beds tonight."

The landlord was right. They did not want to be on their own.

The next morning, the four men met in Number 12. The landlord wanted to look under the floor near the wall between Numbers 12 and 14. Maybe you think the bones of Nicolas Francken were there. But no, there was just a small metal box. Inside, there was a piece of paper with some strange writing on it. Was this the answer to the mystery of room Number 13?

But nobody could understand the writing – they did not know the language or how to read it. Anderson took the box and the paper to the library in Viborg and the librarian kept them there.

_____

My cousin did not tell me this story until a few months later. He was visiting Upsala in Sweden because he wanted to study old papers there, and I was with him.

One day, we were together in the library. I was reading an old paper, and I said, laughing, "Listen to this. Hundreds of years ago, a young student here sold his soul to the devil." I laughed again.

But Anderson did not laugh. He was angry. "Why did he do that? That's a really dangerous thing to do. Didn't the young man know that?"

And then my cousin told me about his visit to the Golden Lion in Viborg and the mystery of room Number 13.

"There was magic in the Golden Lion Hotel because hundreds of years ago it was Nicolas Francken's house," Anderson told me. "Francken's ghost stayed in the house because he sold his soul to the devil."

During-reading questions

WHISTLE AND I'LL COME TO YOU

1 Who is going to come and use the extra bed in Parkins's hotel room?
2 What happens when Parkins goes for a walk before dinner?
3 What happens the first time Parkins blows the whistle? What happens the second time?
4 What does the servant say about the extra bed?
5 What does Colonel Wilson think that Parkins should do with the whistle? Why?
6 Why does Parkins wake up that night?
7 Why does the figure in his room wave its arms in front of it?
8 What happens to the whistle at the end of the story?

KARSWELL'S CURSE

1 Why is Karswell angry with Mr Gayton?
2 Who is Edward Dunning?
3 What does Karswell give Dunning in the library and why?
4 What does Dunning feel under his pillow that night?
5 Where did John meet Karswell? What did Karswell give him?
6 Why does Dunning need to give his piece of paper back to Karswell?
7 Why does Dunning have to look different?
8 Why does the ticket man at the boat think that Karswell is with another person?

THE BURIED CROWN

1 Who comes into the sitting room at Long's hotel?
2 What did people believe about the crown near Seaburgh?
3 What did the Ager family believe?
4 Why does Paxton want Long to check the corridor?
5 Paxton says that the figure has power over his eyes. What does he mean?
6 Why is Paxton cursed?
7 Why did Paxton leave the hotel before Long?
8 What is strange about the second track in the sand?

NUMBER 13

1 Why have a lot of old houses in Viborg gone?
2 How many windows are there in Anderson's room?
3 What is strange about Anderson's room at night?
4 Who does Anderson read about in the library?
5 Why does the landlord not want a room Number 13 at the Golden Lion Hotel?
6 Why does Anderson invite the landlord to have a drink in his room?
7 In Sweden, Anderson's cousin says, "A young student here sold his soul to the devil." Why does he laugh about it, do you think? Why is Anderson angry?
8 Where was Nicolas Francken's house?

After-reading questions

1 What things do people find in the stories and what magic can they do?
2 Which story did you like the most and why? Which one was the most frightening and why?
3 Choose Parkins from "Whistle and I'll Come to You" or Paxton from "The Buried Crown".
How do they feel at the beginning of the story and how do their feelings change?
4 What strange things happen in "Karswell's Curse" to show Karswell's magic?
5 What happens to room Number 13 when the box is gone, do you think? Why?

Exercises

WHISTLE AND I'LL COME TO YOU

1 **Complete these sentences in your notebook, using the words from the box.**

hole	rude	guest	site	serious
	whistle	magic	extra	

1 Professor Parkins is a ...._serious_.......... young man, and he does not like to be ....
2 His hotel room in Burnstow has an .... bed.
3 He plays golf all afternoon with another hotel ....
4 Parkins finds Disney's archaeological .... at the top of the beach.
5 He pulls out a .... from a .... in the ground.
6 There is .... in the whistle.

2 Are these sentences *true* or *false*? Write the correct answers in your notebook.

1 Parkins does not like talking about ghosts because it is frightening. ....*false*..........
2 Parkins uses both of the beds in his room.
3 When Parkins cleans the whistle, he is surprised to see someone outside on the beach.
4 Parkins sees a picture in his head. A man is running towards a white figure.
5 Colonel Wilson sees a horrible white figure in the window of Parkins's room.
6 Parkins nearly falls out of the window.
7 Parkins is angry with Mr Rogers when he arrives the next day.

KARSWELL'S CURSE

3 Match the two parts of the sentences in your notebook.
Example: 1 − e

1 It may be very bad for Edward
2 If I tell the librarians not to speak about Dunning,
3 Everything will be all right,
4 If you'd like to meet him,
5 I don't know

6 If you can give the paper back,
7 If I can't give the paper back to Karswell,
8 If you want to send him a message,

a I'll ask my cousin for Henry Harrington's address.
b I will die.
c if I believe in black magic.
d if you keep away from him.
e if Mr Karswell learns his name.
f then I won't stop you.
g I will have to explain more.
h maybe you can break the curse.

4 Write the question word. Then answer the questions in your notebook.

1 .... *What* .... is Mr Gayton's job?
He publishes books and papers about history.

2 .... reviewed Karswell's paper about the history of black magic?

3 .... did Karswell write a book called *The Mystery of Magic?*

4 .... many times does Dunning see the name John Harrington in an advertisement?

5 .... is Henry Harrington shocked when he reads Karswell's book?

6 On .... day does Dunning think that he is going to die?

7 .... falls off Karswell's seat on the train?

8 .... does the ticket man ask about Karswell's friend?

THE BURIED CROWN

5 Complete these sentences in your notebook with the correct form of the present perfect.

1 "I *'ve / have had* (**have**) a shock."

2 "No one .... ever .... (**see**) an Anglo-Saxon crown."

3 "You .... (**find**) something amazing."

4 "I .... (**make**) someone angry by touching it!"

5 "You .... (**do**) it," Long said. "You .... (**put**) the crown back safely."

6 "You .... (**be**) very kind."

7 " .... you .... (**see**) Mr Paxton?" Long asked a servant.

8 "He .... (**go**) out," the servant replied.

6 Choose the correct adjective from the box to complete the sentences about people from the story in your notebook.

| worried | terrified | exciting | amazed | shocked |
| interested | frightened | amazing |

1 At the church, an old man asks Paxton, "Are you
......*interested*........ in our old stories?"
2 At first, Paxton thinks that the idea of looking for the buried crown is ....
3 William Ager was very .... that there was no one to keep the crown safe after he died.
4 Long thinks that it is .... to find an Anglo-Saxon crown.
5 When Long sees the crown, he is ....
6 When they get to the trees on the hill, Paxton is ....
7 Long is .... when he studies the second track in the sand.
8 Long is very .... to think that Paxton is running after this figure.

NUMBER 13

7 Match the names to the sentences in your notebook.

| the servant | Anderson | Jensen | the landlord |
| Nicolas Francken | Anderson's cousin |

1 He is telling the story. *Anderson's cousin*
2 He studies old church books and papers.
3 He sold his soul to the devil.
4 He is staying in room Number 14.
5 He thinks that the number 13 is unlucky.
6 He tries to break the door of Number 13.

8 **Put the sentences in the correct order in your notebook.**

a ....Anderson sees the shadow of a man in room Number 13.

b ....The servant hits the door of Number 13 with a metal bar.

c ....Mr Jensen hurries into Anderson's room because someone is singing.

d ....*1*....Nicolas Francken sold his soul to the devil.

e ....Anderson tells his cousin about the mystery of Number 13 at the Golden Lion Hotel.

f ....Anderson listens in the corridor and hears a noise inside room Number 13.

g ....A horrible arm with long grey hair comes out of room Number 13.

h ....Anderson reads that Nicolas Francken suddenly went away.

ALL STORIES

9 **Write the past tense of these irregular verbs in your notebook.**

1 blow ....*blew*............

2 break

3 choose

4 fall

5 hold

6 hurry

7 keep

8 lay

9 lose

10 send

11 stand

12 throw

10 **Choose the correct verbs from Exercise 9 to complete these sentences in your notebook.**

1 When Parkins ....*blew*............ the whistle, the wind came.
2 The horrible figure .... between the two beds in Parkins's hotel room.
3 John Harrington .... out of a tree and .... his neck.
4 John Harrington .... his programme at a concert.
5 The doctor .... Dunning's servants to hospital.
6 When Dunning heard a door open at night, he .... out to the corridor.
7 Paxton .... the crown on the bed.
8 Long .... Paxton's coat while he found the right place in the ground.
9 Anderson .... the Golden Lion Hotel because it was a beautiful building.
10 The librarian in Viborg .... the box and the paper with the strange writing.

Project work

1 Which story did you like best? Write a review of it.
2 Choose one of the stories and write a different ending.
3 What happens when Parkins goes back to Cambridge and tells Disney about the archaeological site? Write their conversation. ("Whistle and I'll Come to You")
4 Write a letter from Edward Dunning to Mr and Mrs Gayton to tell them about Karswell. ("Karswell's Curse")
5 You are a police officer. Write questions to ask Long. ("The Buried Crown")
6 Write a newspaper story about the Golden Lion Hotel. ("Number 13")

Glossary

advertisement (n.)
An *advertisement* tells people about something. Then they might buy or use it. You can see *advertisements* in the street, on TV or on a website.

amazing (adj.); **amazed** (adj.)
An *amazing* thing is very good or wonderful. If you are *amazed*, you are very surprised.

Anglo-Saxon (n.)
one of a group of people in the past. They lived in England about a thousand years ago.

archaeology (n.);
archaeological (adj.);
archaeologist (n.)
Archaeologists find old things under the ground. They study these old things. This is *archaeology*. An *archaeologist* works on an *archaeological* site.

believe (v.)
to be sure that something is true

believe in (phr. v.)
to be sure that something is real

black magic (n.)
If a person does *black magic*, they use *magic powers* to do bad things.

blow (v.) (past tense **blew**)
Wind *blows* when it moves strongly.

bury (v.); **buried** (adj.)
to put a thing under the ground. Then that thing is *buried*.

church (n.)
People love God and they meet in a building. This is a *church*. The *Church* is also a group of people. They own all the churches in the country and the things inside them.

colonel (n.)
a person with an important job in the army (= a group of soldiers)

corridor (n.)
a long room with doors to other rooms

curse (n.); **cursed** (adj.)
Someone puts a *curse* on you and bad things happen to you. Then you are *cursed*.

earth (n.)
the ground under plants and roads. Flowers and plants grow in *earth*.

extra (adj.)
An *extra* thing is one more than you need.

figure (n.)
You can see a person, but you cannot see their face. This is a *figure*.

guardian (n.)
a person who keeps a child or a thing safe

guest (n.)
a person in a hotel or visiting your house

history (n.); **historian** (n.)
History is information about the past. A *historian* studies *history*.

hole (n.)
a place in the ground with no *earth*. You can *bury* things in a *hole*.

hurry (v.)
to do something or move fast

landlord (n.)
a *landlord* owns a small hotel

librarian (n.)
A *librarian* works in a library.

magic (n.)
in stories, *magic* is a *power*. Strange things can happen with *magic*.

mist (n.)
When there is *mist*, the air is wet and grey, and you cannot see very well.

mystery (n.)
If you cannot explain something, it is a *mystery*.

nervous (adj.); **nervously** (adv.)
If you are *nervous*, you are worried because you think that something bad will happen. If you do something *nervously*, you do it slowly because you are *nervous*.

paper (n.)
an important piece of writing about *history* or language, for example

power (n.)
A person or thing has special *powers*. They can do *magic*.

professor (n.)
an important teacher at a university

publish (v.)
to make and sell books and *papers*

review (v. and n.)
If you *review* a book, you read it and write or speak about it. You decide if it is good or bad. This is a *review*.

rude (adj.)
not acting in a nice way

serious (adj.); **seriously** (adv.)
A *serious* person does not smile or laugh very often. When someone is *seriously* ill, they are very ill.

sheet (n.)
Sheets are very thin. You put a *sheet* on a bed and then you lie on it.

shock (n.); **shocked** (adj.)
You have a *shock* when you suddenly feel a pain. You are *shocked* when you are very surprised because something bad has happened.

site (n.)
Something happens at a *site*. For example, people build on a building *site* and do *archaeology* on an *archaeological site*.

soul (n.)
Many people think that we all have a *soul*. You cannot see a person's *soul*. It stays in this world after the person dies.

subject (n.)
1) You talk about a *subject*, for example, the weather.
2) You study a *subject*, for example, *history* or *archaeology*.

terrified (adj.)
very frightened

unlucky (adj.)
People believe that some things are *unlucky*. For example, they think that if you see the number 13 or a black cat, bad things will happen.